MUSIC
for
EAR TRAINING

MUSIC
for
EAR TRAINING

FOURTH EDITION

Michael Horvit   Timothy Koozin   Robert Nelson
Moores School of Music, University of Houston

❖❖ CENGAGE

Australia • Brazil • Mexico • Singapore • United Kingdom • United States

Music for Ear Training, **Fourth Edition**
Michael Horvit, Timothy Koozin,
Robert Nelson

Product Director: Laura Ross

Product Manager: Kori Alexander

Learning Designer: Emma Guiton

Content Manager: Mary Ann Lidrbauch

Marketing Manager: Laura Kuhlman

Product Assistant: Hannah Ells

Digital Delivery Lead: Matt Altieri

IP Analyst: Ann Hoffman

Designer, Creative Studio: Nadine Ballard

Production Service: MPS Limited

Cover Designer: Wing-ip Ngan, Inkdesign, Inc.

Cover Image: Mike Kemp/Getty Images;
Datacraft Co. Ltd./Getty Images

Compositor: MPS Limited

For product information and technology assistance, contact us at
Cengage Customer & Sales Support, 1-800-354-9706 or
support.cengage.com.

For permission to use material from this text or product,
submit all requests online at
www.cengage.com/permissions.

Library of Congress Control Number: 2019911115

Student Edition:
ISBN: 978-0-357-10684-6

Loose-leaf Edition:
ISBN: 978-0-357-10686-0

Annotated Instructor's Edition:
ISBN: 978-0-357-44172-5

Cengage
200 Pier 4 Boulevard
Boston, MA 02210
USA

Cengage is a leading provider of customized learning solutions with employees residing in nearly 40 different countries and sales in more than 125 countries around the world. Find your local representative at **www.cengage.com**.

Cengage products are represented in Canada by Nelson Education, Ltd.

To learn more about Cengage platforms and services, register or access your online learning solution, or purchase materials for your course, visit **www.cengage.com**.

Printed in the United States of America
Print Number: 01   Print Year: 2019

Contents

UNIT 2

UNIT 3

UNIT 4

UNIT 5

UNIT 6

UNIT 7

UNIT 8

UNIT 9

UNIT 10

UNIT 11

UNIT 12

UNIT 13

UNIT 14

UNIT 15

UNIT 16

UNIT 17

Contents

Getting Started

1. Log in to your MindTap for *Music for Ear Training* course, following the instructions on the card included with your book. Do not lose the access code printed on the card. Only registered users have full access to the MindTap.

2. Begin your online practice immediately within MindTap for *Music for Ear Training*.

What's New in Music for Ear Training, Version 4.0

- All listening examples have been moved to MindTap, the platform that propels students from memorization to mastery.

- New streaming audio for all music listening examples, rendered with the highest-quality instrumental timbres sampled from all the principal instruments of the orchestra. Listening exercises within MindTap are compatible with popular Web browsers for computers and mobile tablets, but scrumming (the ability to adjust an audio file to start playing at a time stamp other than 0:00) is only fully supported in Edge and Firefox browsers. To scrum in Chrome, students will need to download the musical clip by clicking the vertical ... button within the file. The Safari browser does not support scrumming.

- New Web-based preliminary exercises for intervals, chords, and scales to help students acquire strong listening skills in music fundamentals. Contextual listening examples provide opportunities to hear intervals and chords in musical contexts with scales, melodies, and varied instrumental timbres. An online record tracks the student's personal progress.

- A new unit of music literature examples for twentieth-century techniques, with excerpts for dictation from works by major modern composers including Debussy, Bartok, Stravinsky, Schoenberg, and others.

Suggestions to the Instructor

Log in to MindTap and get access to a full suite of resources, including a robust number of listening exercises for dictation, designed to propel your students from memorization to mastery in Ear Training.

Often, there is not sufficient class time to provide students with the reinforcing experiences necessary to develop the tools to take music dictation with ease, assurance, and fluency. The ability to write down music after hearing it is an extremely important skill that benefits the musician in numerous ways. It enhances one's aural acuity both as a performer and listener and makes all musical experiences more vivid and comprehensible.

This interactive material provides each individual student with the equivalent of a private ear-training tutor. Each student may proceed at his or her own pace. Examples and portions of examples can be listened to as often as necessary for each individual to master the material. Isolated lines in four-part examples and right-hand or left-hand parts in keyboard textures can be selected as listening options. *It is important, however, that the student develop the ability to take down dictation accurately within a limited number of replays*, possibly four, or other number recommended by the instructor.

MindTap for *Music for Ear Training* delivers musical listening examples rendered with the highest-quality orchestral and keyboard sampled sounds. The layout of the workbook pages is designed in parallel with the listening examples, so that the student can write dictation directly onto the appropriate page. Formatted staves with time and key signatures and bar lines are provided for each example. Answers for all practice dictation examples are immediately available on-screen by selecting "Check My Work." Answers for the quizzes at the end of each chapter are available only to the teacher in the Instructor's Edition of the workbook.

All of the material in *Music for Ear Training* is cumulative. Each chapter builds upon those that have preceded it. We have included the following types of material for dictation:

1. **Rhythmic exercises** are played on a single pitch and provide practice with specific rhythmic problems.

2. **Melodic exercises** are composed in a musical way and deal with specific scalar, harmonic, and rhythmic material. In most chapters, preliminary as well as full-length exercises are provided.

3. **Harmonic exercises** are played in four-voice texture, either choral or keyboard. They focus on particular chordal vocabulary. In most chapters, preliminary as well as full-length exercises are provided.

4. **Quizzes** are included in each chapter after the exercises in each of the above topics.

5. **Music from the literature**. At strategic points throughout *Music for Ear Training*, chapters containing cumulative examples from the literature in a variety of textures are included.

The number of exercises within each unit was dictated by the desire to present both a sufficient number of exercises and a few more challenging exercises for the advanced students. It is, of course, not necessary to do each and every exercise. The instructor may even wish to assign only certain exercises within the quizzes or may wish to mix items from the rhythmic, melodic, and harmonic exercises.

The Unit 1 listening exercises present intervals and chords in musical contexts with scales and melodies. The record of activity maintained for each student may be useful as a personal guide to the students in determining when they have acquired a foundation in the aural study of rudiments that will contribute to success in Unit 1 quizzes and the dictations that follow in later units. The MindTap also gives the student the opportunity for virtually endless drill with intervals, qualities of triads, and scale types. The student is allowed to determine the range of intervals to hear from a single category—for example, major and minor thirds—up to all intervals. Similarly, the student may elect specific qualities of triads to hear. The practice drills are followed by quizzes that use the formatted sheets in the workbook. Students access the audio for the quizzes using the MindTap. The interval quizzes are graded by interval type, but each quiz contains a section that is cumulative—that is, all intervals to that point are included and in all possible arrangements.

It is not necessary to do Unit 1 in any particular order. Scales can easily precede intervals, for example. Unit 1 should also be considered a resource unit, and students should be encouraged to return to it at any time for review drill, particularly on intervals and triad qualities.

New to this edition is Unit 26, Examples from Music Literature, which contains examples of the literature of the twentieth century. These excerpts exemplify the techniques presented in Units 18 through 25. Composers representing a wide variety of styles are included, ranging from Debussy to Stravinsky and Webern.

Music for Ear Training may be used conveniently with most of the sight singing texts currently available. It is designed in parallel with *Music for Sight Singing* by Thomas Benjamin, Michael Horvit, and Robert Nelson, sixth edition (Schirmer Books, 2013), and will work especially smoothly with the presentation of materials in that book.

The Instructor's Edition is laid out parallel to the Student Edition but with the answers to all of the exercises and quizzes included. The Roman numeral analyses provided for the common-practice examples follow the system used in Thomas Benjamin, Michael Horvit, and Robert Nelson, *Techniques and Materials of Music*, seventh edition (Schirmer, 2008), but instructors should feel free to substitute whatever system they prefer. Lead sheet (jazz) chord symbol usage is also far from uniform, and instructors may wish to specify how they want chords analyzed in Unit 20. Some serial melodies in Unit 25 show accidentals on every note; others use the traditional method. Enharmonic equivalents are occasionally indicated parenthetically, as with tritones in Unit 1. In other places, students may notate certain notes enharmonically, and the instructor will need to determine the correctness of these spellings.

Suggestions to the Student

The MindTap for *Music for Ear Training* provides access to the audio and drills you will use with the Workbook pages. To gain entry, create your MindTap user account. You will need to enter the access code you received on a card included with this book. Simply follow the instructions on the card. After entering your registration information online, you will have full access to the MindTap for *Music for Ear Training*.

The ability to hear and quickly comprehend any piece of music is a skill that is crucial to the musician. Having a "good ear" involves more than just playing or singing in tune. Traditionally, students acquire this skill through the discipline of aural dictation—listening to a musical example and then writing it down. Unfortunately, all too many students approach this facet of their musical studies with trepidation and anxiety. They may assume that only those musicians blessed with perfect pitch can do dictation. In fact, aural comprehension is a skill that can be acquired with diligent, structured practice. *Music for Ear Training* is designed to give the student an ample number of ear-training practice exercises that can be completed outside the classroom and at the student's own pace. The exercises are carefully graded to lead from simple isolated problems, such as interval recognition, all the way to the transcription of short pieces from the literature. You can compare your results with the correct solution by clicking on the "Check my Work" button.

Four categories of exercises appear throughout *Music for Ear Training*:

- Rhythmic dictation drills,

- Preliminary exercises for melodic dictation, which focus on particular musical patterns, and harmonic dictation, which focuses on chord progressions,

- Melodies and phrase-length harmonic exercises, and

- Music from the literature.

Exercises in interval, triad, and scale recognition are contained in the first unit. You can return to this unit for review at any time. As a rule, the preliminary exercises introduce a specific item, such as an interval or a chord, and help you to assimilate that item through drill. The melodies and phrase-length harmonic exercises are cumulative and serve to integrate the new items into the vocabulary previously presented. You can go back and review the interval and triad recognition drills from Unit 1 at any time. The units containing music from the literature will help you to gauge your progress. You will see how facility with the rhythmic, melodic, and harmonic exercises improves your understanding of the music that is the stuff of your day-to-day activities.

Quizzes are included for each unit of the workbook. These quizzes may be given in class or assigned as homework, and your instructor may ask you to submit them either in class or by uploading your completed work through online submission. The solutions for these quizzes are available only to your instructor.

Since aural dictation is often a new experience, it is easy to become overwhelmed. As an aid, we have incorporated at the beginning of most sets of exercises a number of suggestions and strategies for listening. You will also occasionally find specific suggestions preceding certain exercises. Here is a summary of all those general strategies; they will help you to focus your listening and correctly interpret what you hear.

These lists are not intended to exhaust all the possibilities. Your instructor will likely have additional suggestions, and you will discover other useful devices on your own. From time to time, additional suggestions will appear on the screen. These suggestions are intended to help you deal with a particular exercise, but make a note of them because they will come in handy for other exercises as well.

Rudiments

Unit 1 provides exercises for intervals, triads, and scales. Unit 1 exercises in MindTap present intervals and chords within musical contexts of scales and melodies. You can track your progress with an online record of your activity. MindTap allows you to control your practice session with a virtually unlimited number of examples. For intervals, you may elect to concentrate on just one size—say, seconds—or you may elect to listen to as broad a range of interval sizes as you wish. There are similar options with triads and scales. Within MindTap, you may practice with however many listening drills as you like by selecting the checkbox on the left-hand side of the listening drills list. In the Test Overview section, determine the total number of questions you would like to review in one practice test and select "Take Test Now." When you have completed all the listening drills within the practice test you may select "Submit & Review Test" to see which answers are correct, incorrect, or partially correct. You may review your previous attempts in the "Past Attempts" section on the review page. Unit 1 is a valuable resource unit, and you should use it for review at any time. For example, the melodic dictation exercises are graded by interval content, and you may wish to review the particular intervals before working on the melodies. Similarly, when seventh chords are introduced, you might wish to review sevenths.

Rhythmic Dictation

1. Define the time signature (how many beats per measure, simple or compound, and so on), and then listen to the complete exercise.

2. How is the meter defined? Do you hear long notes on strong beats and quicker notes on weak beats? Try tapping the beat as you listen to the example.

3. What is the most frequently occurring note value? Is it the beat unit or a division of the beat? How many different values are there?

4. Do you hear recurring patterns? Are there instances of any particular rhythmic device such as syncopation?

Melodic Dictation

1. Listen to the complete exercise.

2. Establish the key for yourself by listening to either the given scale or the tonic note. (Simply click on the buttons for the scale or the note.)

3. Does the music move by step or by skip? Are the skips large or small? Do consecutive skips arpeggiate a particular chord?

4. What is the shape, or curve, of the melody? It can be helpful to draw a simple graph of its design before writing down the actual pitches.

5. Listen for important structural pitches. These include the first and last pitches, cadential pitches, metric and agogic accents, and the highest and lowest pitches. Try sketching in these pitches first.

6. If you use solfège syllables or scale degree numbers in your singing, then writing these during dictation may also be a helpful strategy.

7. Listen for phrase and cadence structure. What is the form of the melody? Are there interior cadences? Do two phrases form a period? Remember to constantly apply what you have learned in your theory classes. The more you are aware of what is likely to be true, the more you will hear.

8. Do you hear a pattern in the music? This patterning may be rhythmic only, or it may involve both rhythm and pitch. Are patterns repeated or sequenced? Are there recurrences of musical ideas, particularly at the beginning of subsequent phrases?

9. As you listen to a melody, sketch simple symbols to indicate pitches and rhythms; that is, circles for whole and half notes and dots for shorter note values. Allow for proportional distances between note heads to represent values within a measure. Supply precise rhythmic values as a subsequent step, then notate what you hear in final form.

10. An excellent method of enhancing your ability to take melodic dictation is to write down melodies from memory. When taking a break in the practice room or library, think of a tune you already know. It may be a folk, children's, popular, or patriotic song. Pick a key and jot it down. This will strengthen your ability to get material you clearly have in your mind down on paper.

Harmonic Dictation

1. Listen to the complete exercise.

2. For phrase-length exercises, what kind of cadence(s) do you hear?

3. Chord progressions in the common-practice period follow predictable patterns. If you have identified one chord, consider the finite number of possibilities for chords that might logically follow. If you have identified the cadential chords, try working backwards.

4. MindTap allows you to isolate the individual voices. Be sure to use stereo headphones or speakers of good quality, since the online audio relies on stereo separation to isolate voices in some examples. Hearing the lines clearly will help in distinguishing between two chords that are somewhat interchangeable, such as IV and ii6.

Examples from Music Literature

These exercises present actual pieces of music. It should be possible to transcribe these pieces note-for-note. The following suggestions should prove helpful:

1. Listen to the complete exercise.

2. How would you characterize the texture of the music? Are there clear melodic lines? Most piano textures and ensemble textures will have prominent melodies. Focus on these lines that you will be able to isolate.

3. All examples, even those that are contrapuntal, will have obvious harmonic implications. In more homophonic pieces, the chord structures should be quite clear and easily heard as such. Although you will not be required to supply the Roman numerals, harmonic analysis can be a great aid in hearing the music.

4. What is the structure of the music? Do you clearly hear phrase and cadence? What are the cadence types?

   Finally, MindTap will allow you to listen to any one exercise as many times as you wish, and early on in your work, this may be necessary. You should always try, however, to transcribe the music with as few hearings as possible. In most cases, four repetitions should be more than enough. As your skills develop, the number of hearings should decrease. You may elect at any time to see the solution to any of the exercises except for the quizzes. After comparing your solution with that on the screen, you may wish to listen one more time, concentrating on those places where you made mistakes. Keep in mind that scrumming (adjusting an audio file to start playing at a time stamp other than 0:00) is only fully supported in Edge and Firefox browsers. To scrum in Chrome, you will need to download the musical clip by clicking the vertical ... button within the file. The Safari browser does not support scrumming.

The workbook provides you with staff paper already formatted with the correct number of measures for each example along with the key, time signatures, and any given pitches. You may find it useful to use scratch paper for your preliminary sketches, using the workbook only to enter your final version. The workbook pages are easily removed when exercises need to be handed in for evaluation by your instructor. MindTap allows you to download the workbook pages within each exercise to complete your work either by hand or by digital notation software. You may also upload a copy of your completed work via online submission depending on your instructor's preference.

Unit 1 ═══════════════════════════════

Intervals, Triads, and Scales

Use the practice drills within MindTap to prepare for these quizzes.

Major and Minor Seconds: QUIZ NO. 1

Melodic ascending

1. _____   2. _____   3. _____   4. _____   5. _____

Melodic descending

6. _____   7. _____   8. _____   9. _____   10. _____

Harmonic (lower note given)

11. _____   12. _____   13. _____   14. _____   15. _____

Cumulative

(melodic, both ascending and descending, and harmonic)

16. _____   17. _____   18. _____   19. _____   20. _____

21. _____   22. _____   23. _____   24. _____   25. _____

Major and Minor Seconds: QUIZ NO. 2

Melodic ascending

1. _____ 2. _____ 3. _____ 4. _____ 5. _____

Melodic descending

6. _____ 7. _____ 8. _____ 9. _____ 10. _____

Harmonic (lower note given)

11. _____ 12. _____ 13. _____ 14. _____ 15. _____

Cumulative

(melodic, both ascending and descending, and harmonic)

16. _____ 17. _____ 18. _____ 19. _____ 20. _____

21. _____ 22. _____ 23. _____ 24. _____ 25. _____

Name: _____

Major and Minor Thirds: QUIZ NO. 1

Thirds only

Melodic ascending

1. _____ 2. _____ 3. _____ 4. _____ 5. _____

Melodic descending

6. _____ 7. _____ 8. _____ 9. _____ 10. _____

Harmonic

11. _____ 12. _____ 13. _____ 14. _____ 15. _____

Cumulative

16. _____ 17. _____ 18. _____ 19. _____ 20. _____

21. _____ 22. _____ 23. _____ 24. _____ 25. _____

Major and Minor Thirds: QUIZ NO. 2

Thirds only

Melodic ascending

1. _____ 2. _____ 3. _____ 4. _____ 5. _____

Melodic descending

6. _____ 7. _____ 8. _____ 9. _____ 10. _____

Harmonic

11. _____ 12. _____ 13. _____ 14. _____ 15. _____

Cumulative

16. _____ 17. _____ 18. _____ 19. _____ 20. _____

21. _____ 22. _____ 23. _____ 24. _____ 25. _____

Name: _____

Perfect and Augmented Fourths: QUIZ NO. 1

Fourths only

Melodic ascending

1. _____ 2. _____ 3. _____ 4. _____ 5. _____

Melodic descending

6. _____ 7. _____ 8. _____ 9. _____ 10. _____

Harmonic

11. _____ 12. _____ 13. _____ 14. _____ 15. _____

Cumulative

16. _____ 17. _____ 18. _____ 19. _____ 20. _____

21. _____ 22. _____ 23. _____ 24. _____ 25. _____

Perfect and Augmented Fourths: QUIZ NO. 2

Fourths only

Melodic ascending

1. _____   2. _____   3. _____   4. _____   5. _____

Melodic descending

6. _____   7. _____   8. _____   9. _____   10. _____

Harmonic

11. _____   12. _____   13. _____   14. _____   15. _____

Cumulative

16. _____   17. _____   18. _____   19. _____   20. _____

21. _____   22. _____   23. _____   24. _____   25. _____

Perfect and Diminished Fifths: QUIZ NO. 1

Fifths only

Melodic ascending

1. _____   2. _____   3. _____   4. _____   5. _____

Melodic descending

6. _____   7. _____   8. _____   9. _____   10. _____

Harmonic

11. _____   12. _____   13. _____   14. _____   15. _____

Cumulative

16. _____   17. _____   18. _____   19. _____   20. _____

21. _____   22. _____   23. _____   24. _____   25. _____

Perfect and Diminished Fifths: QUIZ NO. 2

Fifths only

Melodic ascending

1. _____ 2. _____ 3. _____ 4. _____ 5. _____

Melodic descending

6. _____ 7. _____ 8. _____ 9. _____ 10. _____

Harmonic

11. _____ 12. _____ 13. _____ 14. _____ 15. _____

Cumulative

16. _____ 17. _____ 18. _____ 19. _____ 20. _____

21. _____ 22. _____ 23. _____ 24. _____ 25. _____

Name: _____

All Perfect Intervals and Tritones: QUIZ NO. 1

Perfect intervals and tritones only

Melodic ascending

1. _____ 2. _____ 3. _____ 4. _____ 5. _____

Melodic descending

6. _____ 7. _____ 8. _____ 9. _____ 10. _____

Harmonic

11. _____ 12. _____ 13. _____ 14. _____ 15. _____

Cumulative

16. _____ 17. _____ 18. _____ 19. _____ 20. _____

21. _____ 22. _____ 23. _____ 24. _____ 25. _____

All Perfect Intervals and Tritones: QUIZ NO. 2

Perfect intervals and tritones only

Melodic ascending

1. _____   2. _____   3. _____   4. _____   5. _____

Melodic descending

6. _____   7. _____   8. _____   9. _____   10. _____

Harmonic

11. _____   12. _____   13. _____   14. _____   15. _____

Cumulative

16. _____   17. _____   18. _____   19. _____   20. _____

21. _____   22. _____   23. _____   24. _____   25. _____

Name: _____

Major and Minor Sixths: QUIZ NO. 1

Sixths only

Melodic ascending

1. _____ 2. _____ 3. _____ 4. _____ 5. _____

Melodic descending

6. _____ 7. _____ 8. _____ 9. _____ 10. _____

Harmonic

11. _____ 12. _____ 13. _____ 14. _____ 15. _____

Cumulative

16. _____ 17. _____ 18. _____ 19. _____ 20. _____

21. _____ 22. _____ 23. _____ 24. _____ 25. _____

Major and Minor Sixths: QUIZ NO. 2

Sixths only

Melodic ascending

1. _____   2. _____   3. _____   4. _____   5. _____

Melodic descending

6. _____   7. _____   8. _____   9. _____   10. _____

Harmonic

11. _____   12. _____   13. _____   14. _____   15. _____

Cumulative

16. _____   17. _____   18. _____   19. _____   20. _____

21. _____   22. _____   23. _____   24. _____   25. _____

Major and Minor Sevenths: QUIZ NO. 1

Sevenths only

Melodic ascending

1. _____ 2. _____ 3. _____ 4. _____ 5. _____

Melodic descending

6. _____ 7. _____ 8. _____ 9. _____ 10. _____

Harmonic

11. _____ 12. _____ 13. _____ 14. _____ 15. _____

Cumulative

16. _____ 17. _____ 18. _____ 19. _____ 20. _____

21. _____ 22. _____ 23. _____ 24. _____ 25. _____

Class: _____   Name: _____

Professor: _____

Major and Minor Sevenths: QUIZ NO. 2

Sevenths only

Melodic ascending

1. _____ 2. _____ 3. _____ 4. _____ 5. _____

Melodic descending

6. _____ 7. _____ 8. _____ 9. _____ 10. _____

Harmonic

11. _____ 12. _____ 13. _____ 14. _____ 15. _____

Cumulative

16. _____ 17. _____ 18. _____ 19. _____ 20. _____

21. _____ 22. _____ 23. _____ 24. _____ 25. _____

Name: _____

All Intervals: QUIZ NO. 1

1. _____ 2. _____ 3. _____ 4. _____ 5. _____

6. _____ 7. _____ 8. _____ 9. _____ 10. _____

11. _____ 12. _____ 13. _____ 14. _____ 15. _____

16. _____ 17. _____ 18. _____ 19. _____ 20. _____

21. _____ 22. _____ 23. _____ 24. _____ 25. _____

All Intervals: QUIZ NO. 2

1. _____ 2. _____ 3. _____ 4. _____ 5. _____

6. _____ 7. _____ 8. _____ 9. _____ 10. _____

11. _____ 12. _____ 13. _____ 14. _____ 15. _____

16. _____ 17. _____ 18. _____ 19. _____ 20. _____

21. _____ 22. _____ 23. _____ 24. _____ 25. _____

Major and Minor Triads: QUIZ NO. 1

1. _____ 2. _____ 3. _____ 4. _____ 5. _____

6. _____ 7. _____ 8. _____ 9. _____ 10. _____

Major and Minor Triads: QUIZ NO. 2

1. _____ 2. _____ 3. _____ 4. _____ 5. _____

6. _____ 7. _____ 8. _____ 9. _____ 10. _____

Name: _____

Introducing Diminished Triads: QUIZ NO. 1

1. _____   2. _____   3. _____   4. _____   5. _____

6. _____   7. _____   8. _____   9. _____   10. _____

Name: _____

Introducing Diminished Triads: QUIZ NO. 2

1. _____ 2. _____ 3. _____ 4. _____ 5. _____

6. _____ 7. _____ 8. _____ 9. _____ 10. _____

Introducing Augmented Triads: QUIZ NO. 1

1. _____ 2. _____ 3. _____ 4. _____ 5. _____

6. _____ 7. _____ 8. _____ 9. _____ 10. _____

Introducing Augmented Triads: QUIZ NO. 2

1. _____   2. _____   3. _____   4. _____   5. _____

6. _____   7. _____   8. _____   9. _____   10. _____

Name: _____

Major and Minor Scales: QUIZ NO. 1

1. _____

2. _____

3. _____

4. _____

5. _____

6. _____

7. _____

8. _____

9. _____

10. _____

Major and Minor Scales: QUIZ NO. 2

1. _____

2. _____

3. _____

4. _____

5. _____

6. _____

7. _____

8. _____

9. _____

10. _____

Unit 2

Rhythmic Dictation: Simple Meters

The goal of this unit is recognition of basic patterns in simple meters. The beat will be established by count-off clicks and the tempo may be adjusted. Listen first to each exercise while counting or tapping the beat. Which notes correspond to the beat? Which notes combine beats into larger values? Be aware of the number of beats per measure. Where do the longer values typically occur?

1.

2.

3.

4.

5.

6.

7.

8.

9.

10.

Class:

Name: _____

Professor:

11.

12.

13.

14.

Rhythmic Dictation: QUIZ NO. 1

1.

2.

3.

4.

5.

Name: _____

Rhythmic Dictation: QUIZ NO. 2

1.

2.

3.

4.

5.

Rhythmic Dictation: QUIZ NO. 3

1.

2.

3.

4.

5.

Melodic Dictation: Seconds, Thirds, and Fourths

Preliminary Exercises

7.

8.

9.

10.

11.

12.

13.

Class:

Professor:

Name: _____

14.

15.

16.

17.

18.

Melodies

This unit contains melodies that are entirely conjunct (stepwise) in motion as well as melodies containing skips of major or minor thirds and perfect fourths. Click the buttons to hear the provided tonic note and scale. Try first singing the appropriate scale to establish a point of reference. Then listen to the melody. Does the music move by step? Is the direction of the line up or down? What scale fragment occurs? What is the pattern of whole and half steps? Do you hear a skip? Concentrate on that interval. Sing the two notes and "fill in" the missing notes. This will tell you if the skip is a third or a fourth. Finally, write out the melody. If you are uncertain about some of the pitches, leave a blank or indicate alternatives. Listen again, filling in the blanks. When you feel confident you have "solved" the melody, listen one last time. Sing along, using syllables, to check your work.

Deliberamente

7.

Moderato

8.

Cantabile

9.

Tempo di Valse

10.

Andante

11.

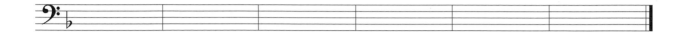

Allegro ma non troppo

12.

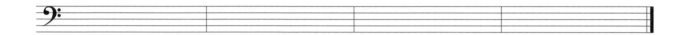

In the last two exercises, you will need to determine both the pitch and the rhythmic value of the first note.

Waltz

13.

Cantabile

14.

Melodic Dictation: QUIZ NO. 1

Allegretto

1.

Andante

2.

Eroico

3.

Allegro

4.

Animato

5.

Melodic Dictation: QUIZ NO. 2

Andante

Moderato

Comodo

Moderato

Giovale

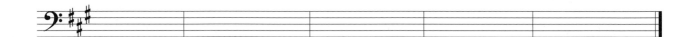

Class:

Professor:

Name: _____

Melodic Dictation: QUIZ NO. 3

Moderato

1.

Allegretto

2.

Andante

3.

Giocoso

4.

Waltz

5.

Melodic Dictation: QUIZ NO. 4

In this quiz you will need to determine both the value and pitch of the initial note.

Lento

1.

Andante

2.

Cantabile

3.

Stately

4.

Semplice

5.

Unit 3

Melodic Dictation: Fifths, Sixths, and Octaves

Preliminary Exercises

1.

2.

3.

4.

5.

6.

7.

8.

9.

10.

11.

12.

13.

14.

15.

16.

17.

18.

Melodies

These melodies introduce consecutive skips outlining the tonic triad and also introduce larger skips of fifths, sixths, and octaves. As before, establish the key by singing the scale. You may also wish to sing the tonic triad. Then listen to the melody. Is the motion by step or by skip? Are there consecutive skips outlining a triad? What is the lowest note? The highest? Isolate the arpeggiation and check with syllables. Check the larger skips by isolating the interval and "filling in" the missing notes.

Moderato

1.

Marziale

2.

Andantino

3.

Dolce

4.

Cantabile

5.

Moderato

6.

Allegro moderato

7.

Grazioso

8.

Allegretto

9.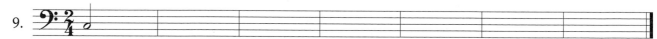

Largamente

10.

Con moto

11.

Cantabile

12.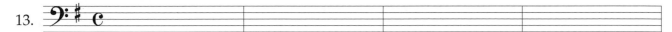

You will need to determine the first pitch for the last two exercises.

Andante

13.

Lento ma non troppo

14.

Class:

Name: _____

Professor:

Melodic Dictation: QUIZ NO. 1

Allegretto

1.

Allegro

2.

Lento

3.

Moderato

4.

Largamente

5.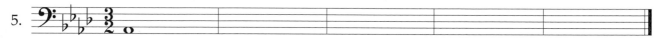

Melodic Dictation: QUIZ NO. 2

Allegro

1.

Cantabile

2.

Moderato

3.

Vivo

4.

Tranquillo

5.

Melodic Dictation: QUIZ NO. 3

Grazioso

1.

Andante

2.

Moderato assai

3.

Allegro ma non troppo

4.

Cantabile

5.

Melodic Dictation: QUIZ NO. 4

Maestoso

1.

Andantino

2.

Spiritoso

3.

Allegretto

4.

Moderato

5.

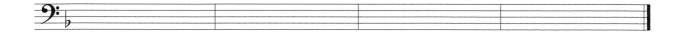

Class: _____

Name: _____

Professor: _____

Harmonic Dictation: Four-Part Settings of the Tonic Triad

The tonic triad is presented with all the possibilities of soprano-line motion. Since all the chords are in root position, you can easily fill in the bass line. Listen then for the direction of the soprano line. What is the melodic interval from one note to the next? Since the soprano will itself outline the tonic triad it should be easy to work out. Finally, fill in the inner voices, paying particular attention to the rules of part-writing.

1.

2.

3.

4.

5.

6.

7.

8.

9.

Class:

Professor:

Name: _____

Harmonic Dictation: QUIZ NO. 1

1.

2.

3.

Harmonic Dictation: QUIZ NO. 2

1.

2.

3.

Class: _____

Name: _____

Professor: _____

Harmonic Dictation: QUIZ NO. 3

1.

2.

3.

Name: _____

Unit 4 ═══════════════════════════════════

Rhythmic Dictation: 2:1 Subdivisions of the Beat

These exercises introduce simple divisions of the beat. As before, listen to the example while you count or tap the beat. Where is the beat divided? Where do multiple beat values occur? Sketch out your solution, then listen again while counting or tapping your solution. How does it compare? Correct any errors.

1.

2.

3.

4.

5.

6.

7.

8.

9.

10.

11.

12.

13.

14.

15.

16.

Class:

Professor:

Name: _____

Rhythmic Dictation: QUIZ NO. 1

1.

2.

3.

4.

5.

Name: _____

Rhythmic Dictation: QUIZ NO. 2

1.

2.

3.

4.

5.

Class:

Professor:

Name: _____

Rhythmic Dictation: QUIZ NO. 3

1.

2.

3.

4.

5.

Melodic Dictation: The Tonic Triad and Dominant Seventh

Preliminary Exercises

1.

2.

3.

4.

5.

6.

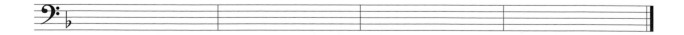

Class:

Name: _____

Professor:

7.

8.

9.

10.

Melodies

These exercises introduce the dominant seventh chord. As before, first establish the key by singing the scale along with the arpeggiations of the I, V, and V7 chords. Then listen to the example. Where do skips occur? Are there consecutive skips outlining a chord? Which chord is it? What is the lowest note of the arpeggiation? The highest?

Allegretto

1.

Poco animato

2.

Allegro

3.

Semplice

4.

5.

6.

7.

8.

9.

Andante cantabile

10.

Giocoso

11.

Minuet

12.

Marziale

13.

Andante

14.

Cantabile

15.

Allegro assai

16.

Melodic Dictation: QUIZ NO. 1

Moderato

1.

Grazioso

2.

With determination

3.

Adagietto

4.

Ländler

5.

Melodic Dictation: QUIZ NO. 2

Semplice

1.

Ben marcato

2.

Cantabile

3.

Giocoso

4.

Allegro ma non troppo

5.

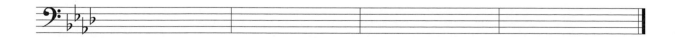

Melodic Dictation: QUIZ NO. 3

Con moto

1.

Allegretto

2.

Moderato

3.

Allegro

4.

Andantino

5.

Melodic Dictation: QUIZ NO. 4

Minuet

1.

Moderato

2.

Con brio

3.

Cantabile

4.

Espressivo

5.

Harmonic Dictation: The Tonic Triad and Dominant Seventh

Basic Progressions

G: I

D: I

B♭: I

F: V

5.

A: V

6.

A♭: V

7.

E♭: I

8.

D: I

9.

B♭: I

10.

D: I

11.

G: I

12.

C: I

13.

F: V⁷

14.

E: V⁷

15.

E♭: V⁷

16.

B♭: V⁷

17.

G: V

18.

B♭: I

19.

A: V

20.

E♭: V⁷

21.

C: I

22.

D: I

23.

A♭: I

24.

A: I

25.

F: I

26.

E: V

27.

C: I

28.

E: I

29.

F: V

30.

G: I

31.

A♭: V

32.

D: V^7

33.

Bb: V⁷

34.

Eb: I

35.

F: I

36.

A: V

Phrase-Length Exercises

These exercises present a variety of connections of tonic and dominant. Concentrate on chord pairs. (The basic progressions will provide you a secure point of reference and should be mastered first!) Is the second chord of the pair the same or different? If it is the same, apply the skills acquired in Unit 3. If different, concentrate on the outer voices. Does the bass skip up or down? Fill in the bass line. Does the soprano move in similar or contrary motion? By step or by skip? Fill in the soprano, then complete the inner voices, paying particular attention to the rules of voice leading. With phrase-length exercises, listen for the degree of closure. Does the phrase end on tonic (authentic cadence) or dominant (half cadence)? If the phrase ends with an authentic cadence, is it perfect or imperfect?

5.

G: I

6.

F: I

7.

E: I

8.

D: I

9.

Ab: I

10.

Ab: I

Class:

Professor:

Name: _____

Harmonic Dictation: QUIZ NO. 1

1.

    D: I

2.

    G: I

3.

    F: I

4.

    B♭: I

5.

    A: I

Class: _____   Name: _____

Professor: _____

Harmonic Dictation: QUIZ NO. 2

1.

A: I

2.

E♭: V

3.

D: I

4.

C: I

5.

B♭: I

Class:

Professor:

Name: _____

Harmonic Dictation: QUIZ NO. 3

1.

A: I

2.

F: I

3.

G: I

4.

A♭: I

5.

E: I

Harmonic Dictation: QUIZ NO. 4

1.

A♭: V

2.

D: I

3.

A: I

4.

B♭: I

5.

G: I

Unit 5

Rhythmic Dictation: 4:1 Subdivision of the Beat, Anacruses

> These exercises introduce subdivisions of the beat. As before, listen to the example while counting or tapping the beat. Where do the subdivisions occur? How many notes are there within a beat? What pattern do you hear?

1.

2.

3.

4.

5.

6.

7.

8.

9.

10.

11.

12.

13. $\frac{4}{8}$

14. $\frac{3}{8}$

15. $\mathbf{c}$

16. $\frac{2}{4}$

Rhythmic Dictation: QUIZ NO. 1

1.

2.

3.

4.

5.

Class:

Name: _____

Professor:

Rhythmic Dictation: QUIZ NO. 2

1.

2.

3.

4.

5.

Name: _____

Rhythmic Dictation: QUIZ NO. 3

1.

2.

3.

4.

5.

Name: _____

Melodic Dictation: Primary Triads and the Dominant Seventh

Preliminary Exercises

Name: _____

Melodies

These exercises contain patterns implying all the primary triads (I, IV, and V) and the dominant seventh. For each example, establish the key by singing the scale and the arpeggiations of each triad. As you listen, determine whether the line is moving by step or skip. If by step, what is the scale fragment? Focus on the framing pitches (lowest and highest of the scale fragment). If by skip, which triad is being arpeggiated? Again, concentrate on establishing the lowest and highest notes.

Not too fast

1.

Cantabile

2.

Moderato

3.

Andante

4.

Allegro

5.

Giocoso

6.

Andantino

7.

Allegretto

8.

Moderato

9.

Allegro

10.

Tempo giusto

11.

Animato

12.

Larghetto

13.

Allegretto

14.

Leggiero

15.

March

16.

Melodic Dictation: QUIZ NO. 1

Spiritoso
1.

Grazioso
2.

Ländler
3.

Marziale
4.

Moderato
5.

Name: _____

Melodic Dictation: QUIZ NO. 2

Waltzer

1.

Moderato

2.

Allegro moderato

3.

Allegro

4.

Allegretto

5.

Name: _____

Melodic Dictation: QUIZ NO. 3

Allegretto

1.

Tempo di valse

2.

Semplice

3.

Cantabile

4.

Allegro

5.

Class: _____

Name: _____

Professor: _____

Melodic Dictation: QUIZ NO. 4

Spiritoso

1.

Allegro ma non troppo

2.

Andantino

3.

Spiritoso

4.

Dolce

5.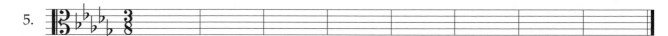

Harmonic Dictation: Primary Triads and the Dominant Seventh; Cadential Tonic Six-Four

Basic Progressions

Primary triads and the dominant seventh

1.

A: I

2.

C: IV

3.

B: I

4.

E: IV

5.

B♭: I

6.

B♭: I

7.

F: V

8.

E♭: I

9.

D: I

10.

B♭: I

Cadential tonic six-four

11.

E: I

12.

D♭: I

13.

C: I

14.

D: I

15.

A♭: I

16.

G: I

Phrase-Length Exercises

These exercises present all the primary triads and introduce the cadential six-four chord. As before, you should drill on the preliminary exercises. Then, listen to each phrase-length exercise, concentrating on the cadential progression. Do you hear an authentic cadence or a half cadence? Establish the goal chord and work backwards. What are the most likely chords to occur at the cadence? Is a dominant preparation (pre-dominant) chord used? A cadential six-four?

Eb: I

D: I

B: I

E: I

5.

A: I

6.

F: I

7.

D♭: I

8.

G: I

Class: _____ Name: _____

Professor: _____

9.

Db: I

10.

G: I

Class:

Professor:

Name: _____

Harmonic Dictation: QUIZ NO. 1

1.

E: I

2.

F: I

3.

D: I

4.

A♭: I

5.

G: I

Harmonic Dictation: QUIZ NO. 2

1.

    G: I

2.

    B♭: I

3.

    C: I

4.

    D♭: I

5.

    E♭: I

Class:

Name: _____

Professor:

Harmonic Dictation: QUIZ NO. 3

1. Db: I

2. A: I

3. Eb: I

4. D: I

5. B: I

Harmonic Dictation: QUIZ NO. 4

1.

E: I

2.

F: I

3.

A: I

4.

E: I

5.

A♭: V

Name: _____

Unit 6

Rhythmic Dictation: Dots and Ties

Listen to each example while counting or tapping the beat. Focus on the division and subdivision of the beat. How many smaller values are contained within a given note? Listen for patterns of long and short note values. Will notes of longer duration require a dot or tie?

1.

2.

3.

4.

5.

6.

7.

8.

9.

10.

11.

12.

13. $\frac{3}{2}$

14. **C**

15. $\frac{2}{4}$

16. **C**

Class:

Professor:

Name: _____

Rhythmic Dictation: QUIZ NO. 1

1.

2.

3.

4.

5.

Rhythmic Dictation: QUIZ NO. 2

1.

2.

3.

4.

5.

Name: _____

Rhythmic Dictation: QUIZ NO. 3

1.

2.

3.

4.

5. $\frac{3}{4}$

Melodic Dictation: Minor Mode

Preliminary Exercises

1.

2.

3.

4.

5.

6.

Melodies

First, drill on the preliminary exercises. Sing the three minor scale forms, using syllables. Which scale forms do you hear in each melody? Does the melody use only one form throughout or all three forms? What determines which form is used?

Grazioso

1.

Andantino

2.

Con forza

3.

Moderato

4.

5.

Moderato

6.

Vigoroso

7.

Energico

8.

Cantabile

9.

Dolce

10.

Adagietto

11.

Deciso

12.

Comodo

13.

Allegro

14.

Espressivo

15.

Con moto

16.

Melodic Dictation: QUIZ NO. 1

Melancholique

1.

Cantabile

2.

Buffo

3.

Adagietto

4.

Valse

5.

Class:

Professor:

Name: _____

Melodic Dictation: QUIZ NO. 2

Adagio

1.

Moderato

2.

Moderato

3.

Allegro

4.

Solenne

5.

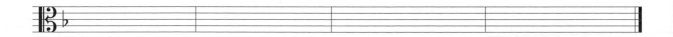

Melodic Dictation: QUIZ NO. 3

Gesangvoll

1.

Andante

2.

Con forza

3.

Grazioso

4.

Geschwind

5.

Name: _____

Melodic Dictation: QUIZ NO. 4

Andante

1.

Grazioso

2.

Doloroso

3.

Con moto

4.

Class: _____   Name: _____

Professor: _____

Ben marcato

5.

Class:

Professor:

Name: _____

Harmonic Dictation: Minor Mode; First Inversion of Triads

Basic Progressions

Minor mode

g: i

e: i

a: i

f♯: i

5.

bb: i   iv

6.

b: i

First inversion of triads

7.

Bb: I

8.

e: i

Class: Name: _____

Professor:

9.

d: V⁶

10.

A: I

11.

f: i

12.

c: i

13.

Bb: I

14.

b: i

15.

A: I

16.

c: i

Class: _____

Name: _____

Professor: _____

Phrase-Length Exercises

As before, drill first on the preliminary exercises. Concentrate on the outer voices. Does the bass move by step or skip? If by skip, is the leap large (fourth or fifth) or small (third)? Sketch in the bass line; this should tell you where inversions occur. After working out the soprano, fill in the inner voices, paying particular attention to the rules of good part-writing. If the exercise is in the minor mode, what is the quality of the dominant chord? Did you remember to raise the leading tone?

1.

g: i

2.

A: I

3.

g: i

4.

A: I

5.

b♭: i

6.

G: I

7.

b: i

8.

E♭: I

9.

e: i

10.

f: i

11.

g: i

12.

B: I

Class: _____

Name: _____

Professor: _____

Harmonic Dictation: QUIZ NO. 1

1.

    f: i

2.

    b: i

3.

    F: I

4.

    a: i

5.

    B: I

Class: Name: _____

Professor:

Harmonic Dictation: QUIZ NO. 2

1.

  d: V⁶

2.

  b♭: i

3.

  B♭: I

4.

  c: i

5.

  D: I

Class:

Professor:

Name: _____

Harmonic Dictation: QUIZ NO. 3

d: i

G: I ___

f: i

A: I

5.

c: i

Class:

Professor:

Name: _____

Harmonic Dictation: QUIZ NO. 4

1.

b: i

2.

E: I

3.

A♭: I

4.

B: I⁶

5.

  c: i

Unit 7

Melodic Dictation: The Supertonic Triad

Preliminary Exercises

1. (music staff, bass clef)

2. (music staff, treble clef)

3. (music staff, treble clef)

4. (music staff, treble clef)

5. (music staff, bass clef)

6. (music staff, bass clef)

Melodies

Sing the supertonic triad in both modes, using syllables. What is its quality in each mode? Where will the supertonic triad most likely occur? Which chord is most likely to follow? How is the underlying progression expressed melodically?

Cantabile

1.

Andante

2.

Valse triste

3.

Tempo di Polka

4.

Leggiero

5.

Lively

6.

Giocoso

7.

Lento

8.

Allegro moderato

9.

Amoroso

10.

Spiritoso

11.

Grave

12.

Zart

13.

Allegretto

14.

Melodic Dictation: QUIZ NO. 1

Andantino

1.

Ländler

2.

Grazioso

3.

Allegro

4.

Andante

5.

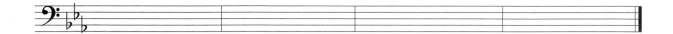

Class:

Professor:

Name: _____

Melodic Dictation: QUIZ NO. 2

Con anima

1.

Doloroso

2.

Andantino

3.

Allegro spiritoso

4.

Adagio

5.

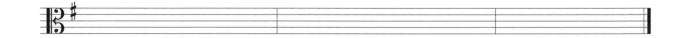

Melodic Dictation: QUIZ NO. 3

Animato

1.

Comodo

2.

Allegro

3.

Cantabile

4.

Allegro con brio

5.

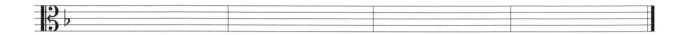

Name: _____

Melodic Dictation: QUIZ NO. 4

Andante

1.

Cantabile

2.

Allegretto

3.

Piacevole

4.

Passionato

5.

Harmonic Dictation: The Supertonic Triad; Inversions of V7

Basic Progressions

Supertonic triad

1.

Bb: I

2.

b: i

3.

C: I

4.

Eb: I

Class:

Professor:

Name: _____

5.

A: I

6.

e: i

7.

c: i

8.

F: I

9.

b: i

Inversions of V7

10.

    F: I

11.

    c: i

12.

    G: I

13.

    B♭: I

14.

E♭: I

15.

E: I

16.

a: i

17.

d: i

18.

A♭: I

Phrase-Length Exercises

These exercises introduce the supertonic triad and present inversions of the V7. As before, concentrate on the bass line. Does it move by step or skip? If by step, in which direction? What harmonic idioms using inversions of the V7 are suggested by the particular sequence of the scale degrees in the bass? As always, master the preliminary exercises before proceeding to the phrase-length exercises.

1.

F: I

2.

e: i

3.

E: I

4.

G: I

Class:

Professor:

Name: _____

B: I

f: i

B♭: I

c: i

B: I

10.

c: i

11.

e: i

12.

f#: i

Class:

Professor:

Name: _____

Harmonic Dictation: QUIZ NO. 1

1.

B: I

2.

c: i

3.

G:I

4.

A: I

5.

a: i

Name: _____

Harmonic Dictation: QUIZ NO. 2

1.

    g: i

2.

    E♭: I

3.

    G: I

4.

    c: i

5.

E: I

Class: _____

Name: _____

Professor: _____

Harmonic Dictation: QUIZ NO. 3

1. A: I

2. d: i

3. e: i

4. G♭: I

5.

g: i

Harmonic Dictation: QUIZ NO. 4

1.

e: i

2.

D♭:   V

3.

f#: i

4.

f: i

5.

b: i

Unit 8

Rhythmic Dictation: Compound Meter

This unit introduces compound meter. Listen to each exercise while counting or tapping the beat. Do you feel the triple division of the beat? Within each beat, are there three equal values or long-short? Are notes within the beat themselves divided? Review the common patterns found in compound meter.

1.

2.

3.

4.

5.

6.

7.

8.

9.

10.

11.

12.

13.

14.

15.

16.

Rhythmic Dictation: QUIZ NO. 1

1.

2.

3.

4.

5.

Rhythmic Dictation: QUIZ NO. 2

1.

2.

3.

4.

5.

Rhythmic Dictation: QUIZ NO. 3

1.

2.

3.

4.

5.

Melodic Dictation: All Diatonic Triads

Preliminary Exercises

1.

2.

3.

4.

5.

6.

Class:

Professor:

Name: _____

7.

8.

9.

10.

Class: _____

Name: _____

Professor: _____

Melodies

These melodies contain implications of all the diatonic triads. Review the most common progressions which use the vi (or VI) and iii (or III) chords. Does the melody outline a chord? What are the framing pitches? The pattern of intervals?

Grazioso

1.

Allegretto

2.

Moderato

3.

Andante

4.

Religioso

5.

Allegro, ma non troppo

6.

Animato

7.

Andantino

8.

Flowing

9.

Moderato

10.

Andante   (after Mendelssohn)

11.

Gigue   (after J.S. Bach)

12.

Melodic Dictation: QUIZ NO. 1

Tempo di valse

1.

Allegretto

2.

Moderato

3.

Allegro, ma non troppo

4.

Lento

5.

Melodic Dictation: QUIZ NO. 2

Andante

1.

Espressivo

2.

Giocoso

3.

Andante

4.

Con anima

5.

Melodic Dictation: QUIZ NO. 3

Moderato

1.

Giocoso

2.

Menuetto

3.

4. Adagio

5. Moderato

Class:

Name: _____

Professor:

Melodic Dictation: QUIZ NO. 4

Brightly

1.

Adagio

2.

Moderato

3.

Cantabile

4.

Tempo di Valse

5.

Class: _____   Name: _____

Professor: _____

Harmonic Dictation: All Diatonic Triads

Basic Progressions

G: I

c: i

B: I

e♭: i

5.

Ab: I

6.

b: i

7.

F: I

8.

C: I

9.

Bb: I

10.

A: I

11.

f: i

12.

C: I

13.

A: I

14.

E♭: I

15.

b: i

16.

f♯: i

17.

b♭: i

18.

d: i

Class: _____   Name: _____

Professor: _____

Phrase-Length Exercises

These exercises present progressions using all the diatonic triads. Review the most common progressions containing the vi (or VI) and iii (or III) chords.

1.

F: I

2.

e: i

3.

G: I

4.

F: I

5.

f#: i

6.

E♭: I

7.

f#: i

8.

G: I

9.

C: I

10.

E♭: I

Harmonic Dictation: QUIZ NO. 1

1.

Db: I

2.

A: I

3.

e: i

4.

c#: i

5.

Bb: I

Class: _____

Professor: _____

Name: _____

Harmonic Dictation: QUIZ NO. 2

1.

C: I

2.

f: i

3.

D: I

4.

A♭ : I

5.

A: I

Harmonic Dictation: QUIZ NO. 3

1.

E: I

2.

f: i

3.

E♭: I

4.

D♭: V

5.

g: i

Harmonic Dictation: QUIZ NO. 4

1.

B: I

2.

D: I

3.

A♭: I

4.

E: I

5.

b:i

Unit 9

Rhythmic Dictation: Triplets and Duplets

This unit introduces triplets (in simple meters) and duplets (in compound meters). Listen to each exercise while counting or tapping the beat. Concentrate on those beats where divisions occur. Do you hear two or three notes of even value? Are the beats subdivided? Do you hear even groupings of fours or sixes? Or, do you hear a long-short group? Mentally count the values within the beat. The quarter-eighth note figure and the dotted eighth-sixteenth note figure are frequently confused or mistakenly transcribed. Listen carefully!

1.

2.

3.

4.

5.

6.

7.

8.

9.

10.

11.

12.

This example begins with an upbeat.

13.

14.

15.

16.

Class:

Professor:

Name: _____

Rhythmic Dictation: QUIZ NO. 1

1.

2.

3.

4.

5.

Class: Name: _____

Professor:

Rhythmic Dictation: QUIZ NO. 2

1.

2.

3.

4.

5.

Rhythmic Dictation: QUIZ NO. 3

1. $\begin{array}{c} 6 \\ 16 \end{array}$

2. $\mathbf{C}$

3. $\begin{array}{c} 9 \\ 8 \end{array}$

This example begins with an upbeat.

4. $\begin{array}{c} 3 \\ 8 \end{array}$

5. $\begin{array}{c} 2 \\ 4 \end{array}$

Melodic Dictation: Supertonic and Leading Tone Sevenths

Preliminary Exercises

1.

2.

3.

4.

5.

6.

7.

Melodies

These melodies contain implications of ii7 (iiᴼ7) and viiᴼ7 (viiᴼ7). As before, listen for arpeggiations. Do chord sevenths resolve as expected?

Andante

1.

Giocoso

2.

Moderato

3.

Risoluto

4.

Teneramente

5.

Lento

6.

Cantabile

7.

Moderato

8.

Grazioso

9.

Ruhig

10.

Moderato

11.

Name: _____

Risoluto

12.

Cantabile

13.

Dolore

14.

Andante espressivo

15.

Spiritoso

16.

Melodic Dictation: QUIZ NO. 1

Gesangvoll

1.

Triumphantly

2.

Tempo di Siciliana

3.

Andante

4.

Andante espressivo

5.

Class:

Professor:

Name: _____

Melodic Dictation: QUIZ NO. 2

Maestoso

1.

Cantabile

2.

Allegretto

3.

Andantino

4.

Moderato

5.

Class: _____   Name: _____

Professor: _____

Melodic Dictation: QUIZ NO. 3

Moderato

1.

Lively

2.

Con moto

3.

Cantabile

4.

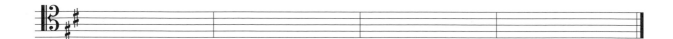

Class:

Name: _____

Professor:

Allegro piacevole

5.

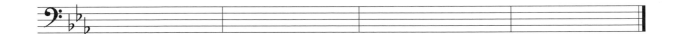

Melodic Dictation: QUIZ NO. 4

Marziale

1.

Moderato

2.

Allegro non troppo

3.

Comodo

4.

Amoroso

5.

Class: _____   Name: _____

Professor: _____

Harmonic Dictation: Supertonic and Leading Tone Sevenths

Basic Progressions

A: I

g: i

3.

C: I

g♯: i

Class:

Professor:

Name: _____

5.

C: I

6.

A: I

7.

D: I

8.

a: i

9.

       c: i

10.

       F: I

11.

       G: I

12.

       B♭: I

13.

e: i

14.

d: i

15.

E♭: I

16.

D: IV

d: i

c#: i

A♭: I

B♭: I

Class: _____

Professor: _____

Name: _____

Phrase-Length Exercises

These exercises contain progressions using ii7 (iiØ7) and viiº7 (viiØ7). As before, listen for the type of cadence. Establish the cadential chords and work backwards. Review the most common progressions involving these chords.

1.

b: i

2.

D:I

3.

F: I

4.

A: I

5.

bb: i

6.

F: I

7.

f#: i

Class: _____   Name: _____

Professor: _____

8.

C: I

9.

B: I

10.

A: I

11.

e♭: i

12.

Bb: I

Class: _____   Name: _____

Professor: _____

Harmonic Dictation: QUIZ NO. 1

1.

    A: I

2.

    d: i

3.

    F: I

4.

    f: i

5.

    e: i

Harmonic Dictation: QUIZ NO. 2

1.

      b: i

2.

      B♭: I

3.

      A: I

4.

      g: i

5.

      E: I

Harmonic Dictation: QUIZ NO. 3

1.

Ab: I

2.

e: i

3.

A: I

4.

g: i

5.

B: I

Harmonic Dictation: QUIZ NO. 4

1.

C: V^6

2.

c: vii$^{\circ 7}$

3.

g: i

4.

b: i

5.

G: I⁶

Unit 10 ━━━━━━━━━━━━━━━

Examples from Music Literature

These exercises present actual musical examples for you to transcribe. At this point, you should be able to transcribe each excerpt completely. Listen to the example first. What is the texture? What kinds of cadences do you hear? Concentrate on individual lines and then listen harmonically. Isolate any unusual rhythmic patterns.

1. Johann Sebastian Bach. Minuet in G

2. Johann Sebastian Bach. *Aus meines Herzens Grunde* (chorale)

3. Johann Sebastian Bach. *Wir glauben all' an einen Gott* (chorale)

4. Ludwig van Beethoven. Six Variations on *Nel cor più non mi sento*

5. Friedrich Kuhlau. Sonatina Op. 88, No. 3, Mvt. III

6. Wolfgang Amadeus Mozart. String Quintet, K. 581 Mvt. IV

Class:

Professor:

QUIZ NO. 1

Joseph Haydn. Sonata in D Major, Hob. XVI:33, Menuetto con Variazioni

Name: _____

QUIZ NO. 2

John Farmer. *Fair Phyllis* (chorale)

Name: _____

QUIZ NO. 3

Wolfgang Amadeus Mozart. String Quartet, K. 80, Mvt. III, Trio

Unit 11

Rhythmic Dictation: Syncopation

This unit introduces syncopation, the displacement of the accent through the occurrence of longer notes on normally weak beats or parts of beats. As always, first listen to each exercise while counting or tapping the beat. Isolate those places where longer values fall off the beat or occur on weak beats. Does the syncopation occur at the beat level or at the division (or subdivision) level? After writing out your solution, check your work by singing along to spot any errors you may have made.

1.

Countoff begins on the downbeat of the incomplete measure.

2.

3.

4.

5.

Class:

Professor:

Name: _____

6.

7.

8.

9.

10.

11.

12.

13. $\begin{array}{c} \mathbf{6} \\ \mathbf{8} \end{array}$ ┃━━━━━━━┃━━━━━━━┃━━━━━━━┃━━━━━━━┃

┃━━━━━━━┃━━━━━━━┃━━━━━━━┃━━━━━━━┃‖

14. $\mathbf{C}$ ┃━━━━━━━┃━━━━━━━┃━━━━━━━┃

┃━━━━━━━┃━━━━━━━┃━━━━━━━┃━━━━━━━┃‖

Rhythmic Dictation: QUIZ NO. 1

1.

2.

3.

4.

5.

Rhythmic Dictation: QUIZ NO. 2

1.

2.

3.

4.

5.

Name: _____

Rhythmic Dictation: QUIZ NO. 3

1.

Countoff begins on the downbeat of the incomplete measure.

2.

3.

4.

5.

Class: _____

Name: _____

Professor: _____

Melodic Dictation: Non-Dominant Seventh Chords

Preliminary Exercises

1.

2.

3.

4.

5.

6.

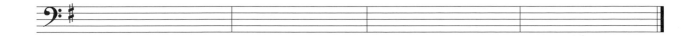

Melodies

After drilling on the preliminary exercises, listen for the implications of non-dominant seventh chords in these melodies. Where do arpeggiations of these seventh chords occur? Do you hear the resolution of the seventh? Sketch out the structural line formed by the chord seventh moving to the note of resolution. Do you hear sequence? What is the underlying progression? Try adding Roman numeral analysis.

Not fast

1.

Cantabile

2.

Giocoso

3.

Comodo

4.

Marziale

5.

Cantabile

6.

Grazioso

7.

Con brio

8.

Gently

9.

Moderato

10.

Andante

11.

Lento

12.

Allegro ma non troppo

13.

Deliberamente

14.

Allegretto

15.

Amoroso

16.

Professor:

Melodic Dictation: QUIZ NO. 1

Raggy

1.

Sospirando

2.

Grazioso

3.

Andantino

4.

Moderato

5.

Name: _____

Melodic Dictation: QUIZ NO. 2

Con forza

1.

Grazioso

2.

Andante espressivo

3.

Ragtime

4.

Amoroso

5.

Class:

Name: _____

Professor:

Melodic Dictation: QUIZ NO. 3

Cantabile

1.

Sea Shanty

2.

Energico

3.

Largo

4.

Giocoso

5.

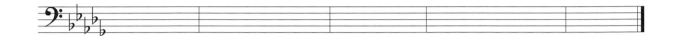

Class: _____   Name: _____

Professor: _____

Melodic Dictation: QUIZ NO. 4

Moderato

1.

Molto espressivo

2.

Giocoso

3.

Molto cantabile

4.

Habanera

5.

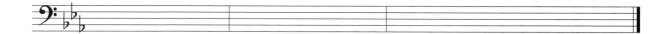

Class: _____

Name: _____

Professor: _____

Harmonic Dictation: Non-Dominant Seventh Chords

Basic Progressions

Eb: I

G: I

a: i

f: i

Class:

Professor:

Name: _____

5.

B: I

6.

f: i

7.

E: I

8.

B♭: I

9.

     D: I

10.

     C: I

Phrase-Length Exercises

Focus on the occurrence of seventh chords. In which voice is the seventh? Does it resolve normally? Concentrate as always on the outer voices.

1.

Bb: I

2.

D: I

3.

Ab: I⁶

4.

A: I

5.

b: i

6.

e: i

7.

A: I

8.

c♯: i

9.

E♭: V   iii⁷

10.

F: I

Harmonic Dictation: QUIZ NO. 1

1.

   B: I

2.

   a: i

3.

   B: I

4.

   B♭: I

5.

   c: i

Class:

Name: _____

Professor:

Harmonic Dictation: QUIZ NO. 2

1.

B♭: I

2.

e: i

3.

f♯: i

4.

G: I

5.

B: I

Harmonic Dictation: QUIZ NO. 3

1.

E: I

2.

g: i

3.

e: V$^7_\sharp$ VI^7

4.

G♭: I   IV^7

A: I

Name: _____

Professor:

Harmonic Dictation: QUIZ NO. 4

1.

g: i⁶

2.

A: I

3.

b♭: V♮

4.

B♭: I

Class:

Professor:

Name: _____

5.

c#: i

Unit 12

Melodic Dictation: Scalar Variants, Modal Borrowing, Decorative Chromaticism

This unit introduces chromatic pitches. *Scalar variants* derive from alterations to the sixth and seventh scale degrees found in the melodic minor scale. *Modal borrowing* involves mixtures of major and minor modal inflection. *Decorative chromaticism* occurs in melodies ornamented with chromatic neighbor or passing tones. After first practicing the Preliminary Exercises, proceed to the melodies. What is the mode? Does the mode change? Where do you hear altered scale degrees or notes not found in the diatonic scale? Sing the scale first to establish a point of reference. Listen for the shape and direction of the line. Do chromatic pitches occur as neighbors or as passing tones?

Preliminary Exercises

Scalar variants

1.

2.

3.

4.

5.

6.

7.

8.

Modal borrowing

9.

10.

11.

12.

13.

14.

15.

16.

Decorative chromaticism

17.

18.

19.

20.

21.

22.

23.

24.

25.

26.

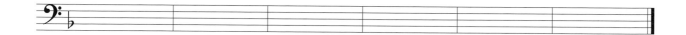

Name: _____

Melodies

Cantabile

1.

Andante

2.

Doloroso

3.

Amoroso

4.

Grazioso

5.

Andantino

6.

Deliberamente

7.

Con moto

8.

Gioviale

9.

Moderato

10.

Marziale

11.

Con moto

12.

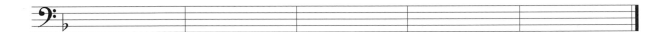

Allegro ma non troppo

13.

Giocoso

14.

Andantino

15.

Espressivo

16.

Andantino

17.

A la marcia

18.

Andante moderato

19.

Allegretto

20.

Class:

Name: _____

Professor:

Melodic Dictation: QUIZ NO. 1

Langsam

1.

Moderato

2.

Andante

3.

A la tango

4.

Con anima

5.

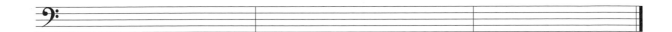

Melodic Dictation: QUIZ NO. 2

Allegro ma non troppo

1.

Marcato

2.

Allegretto

3.

Moderato

4.

Giocoso

5.

Melodic Dictation: QUIZ NO. 3

Lento

1.

Spiritoso

2.

Amabile

3.

Con anima

4.

5.

Con amore

Class:

Name: _____

Professor:

Melodic Dictation: QUIZ NO. 4

Allegretto

1.

Pesante

2.

Flowing

3.

Marziale

4.

Amabile

5.

Melodic Dictation: Scalar Variants, Modal Borrowing, Decorative Chromaticism 289

Harmonic Dictation: Scalar Variants, Modal Borrowing

The harmonic possibilities that arise through altered scale degrees in the minor mode (scalar variants) and borrowed inflections of the minor mode while in a major key (modal borrowing) are explored here. Once you feel confident with the basic progressions found in the Preliminary Exercises, proceed to the Phrase-length Exercises. Where do you hear altered chords? To which chord do they resolve? How do the tendency tones resolve? What kind of cadence do you hear? Establish the cadential chords and work backwards. As always, focus on the outer voices and then fill in the inner voices.

Basic Progressions

Scalar variants

d: i

f♯: i

f: i

c: i

5.

e: i

6.

b: i

7.

d: i

8.

f♯: i

9.

      c#: i

10.

      g: i

Modal borrowing

11.

      D: I

12.

      G: I

Class:

Professor:

Name: _____

13.

E♭: I

14.

E: IV

15.

g: i

16.

D: I

17.

Bb: I

18.

A: I

19.

E: I

20.

d: i

Phrase-Length Exercises

1.

C: I

2.

g: i

3.

D: I

d: V♯

G: I

f♯: i

B♭: I

c: i

9.

F: I

10.

b: i

11.

A: I

12.

E: I

13.

b: i

14.

E: I

Harmonic Dictation: QUIZ NO. 1

1.

E♭: I

2.

d: i

3.

c: V⁶

4.

e: i ___

Name: _____

5.

A: I

Name: _____

Harmonic Dictation: QUIZ NO. 2

1.

        c: i

2.

        A: I

3.

        f: i

4.

        G: I

5.

B♭: I

Class:

Professor:

Name: _____

Harmonic Dictation: QUIZ NO. 3

1.

D:I

2.

e: i

3.

c: i

4.

F: I

5.

A: I

Harmonic Dictation: QUIZ NO. 4

1.

   f: i

2.

   G: I

3.

   e: V♯

4.

   b: i

5.

A: I

Class:

Professor:

Name: _____

Unit 13

Melodic Dictation: Secondary Dominants

For examples of secondary dominant chords in pieces by Bach, Haydn, Chopin, and others, see Unit 14.

Preliminary Exercises

1.

2.

3.

4.

5.

6.

7.

Melodies

This unit requires an understanding of secondary dominant chords. Any major or minor triad may be preceded by its own dominant. Drill on the Preliminary Exercises first to familiarize yourself with the most common progressions. Then, listen to each melody, concentrating on occurrences of chromaticism. Listen for those altered pitches that sound like leading tones. Which scale degrees are being altered? Listen for the partial chromatic scales formed by the structural pitches. You will find it helpful to do a preliminary Roman numeral analysis.

Piacevole

Allegretto

Adagio

Grazioso

Andantino

9.

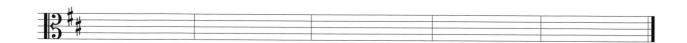

Allegro ma non troppo

10.

Gigue

11.

Siciliano

12.

Eròico

13.

Allegretto

14.

Melodic Dictation: QUIZ NO. 1

Allegretto

1.

Andantino

2.

Moderato

3.

Andante

4.

Scorrevole

5.

Melodic Dictation: QUIZ NO. 2

Comodo

1.

Deliberamente

2.

Cantabile

3.

Adagietto

4.

Moderato

5.

Class:

Name: _____

Professor:

Melodic Dictation: QUIZ NO. 3

1. Allegretto

2. Andantino

3. Moderato

4. Amabile

Giocoso

5.

Class:

Professor:

Name: _____

Harmonic Dictation: Secondary Dominants

Basic Progressions

G: I

B♭: I

c: i

D: I

5.

        f: i

6.

        G: I

7.

        b: i

8.

        E♭: I

9.

A: I

10.

F: I

11.

C: I

12.

c♯: i

Name: _____

Phrase-Length Exercises

After you familiarize yourself with the most common secondary dominant progressions in the Preliminary Exercises, listen to each phrase-length exercise. Where do you hear secondary dominants? To which chord do they resolve? Do you hear a chromatic line in one of the voices? Do secondary dominants occur in sequence? As always, concentrate on the outer voices and then fill in the inner voices. For examples of secondary dominant chords in pieces by Bach, Haydn, Chopin, and others, see Unit 14.

A♭: I

B♭: I

A: I

d: i

5.

D: I

6.

g: i

7.

D♭: I

8.

d: i

9.

e: i

10.

C: I

11.

B♭: I

Class:

Professor:

Name: _____

12.

e: i

13.

E♭: I

14.

a: i

Harmonic Dictation: QUIZ NO. 1

1.

B♭: I

2.

e: i

3.

E♭: I

4.

b: i

5.

D: I

Class:

Professor:

Harmonic Dictation: QUIZ NO. 2

Eb: I

b: i

C: I

4.

Ab: I

5.

G: V   V$^4_2$

Class: _____   Name: _____

Professor: _____

Harmonic Dictation: QUIZ NO. 3

1.

    G: I

2.

    D: V^7

3.

    B♭: I

B♭: I

b: i

Unit 14

Examples from Music Literature

These exercises present actual musical examples for you to transcribe. All contain only the melodic and harmonic vocabulary studied so far and you should be able to transcribe each item completely. Listen to the example first. What is the texture? What kinds of cadences do you hear? Concentrate on individual lines and then listen harmonically. Isolate the altered chords. What are their functions? Is there decorative chromaticism?

1. Johann Sebastian Bach. *Herr, wie du willst, so shick's mit mir* (chorale)

2. Johann Sebastian Bach. *Jesu, meiner Seelen Wonne* (chorale)

3. Johann Sebastian Bach. *Wer nur den lieben Gott läßt walten* (chorale)

4. Johann Sebastian Bach. Minuet in G Minor

5. Edward MacDowell. *To a Wild Rose*, Op. 51, No. 1

Name: _____

6. Carl Maria von Weber. German Dance

7. Frederic Chopin. Valse, Op. 69, No. 1

8. Wolfgang Amadeus Mozart. String Quartet, K. 158, mvt. I

Name: _____

9. Joseph Haydn. Divertimento in D

10. Ludwig van Beethoven. String Quartet, Op. 18, No. 6, mvt. I

QUIZ NO. 1

1. Johann Sebastian Bach. *Jesu, meiner Seelen Wonne* (chorale)

2. Johann Sebastian Bach. *Es woll' uns Gott genadig sein* (chorale)

QUIZ NO. 2

1. Ludwig van Beethoven. *Romanze* from Sonatina in G

2. Frederic Chopin. Prelude, Op. 28, No. 7

QUIZ NO. 3

Joseph Haydn. Divertimento in G, Hob. II:3

Unit 15

Melodic Dictation: Modulation to Closely Related Keys

Melodies

These exercises will challenge and develop your awareness of tonal centers. What is the original key? How is it established? Where does the key change? What devices are employed to effect the key change? Is the new key confirmed cadentially? Analyze the melody, using roman numerals. For examples of modulation to closely related keys in pieces by Bach, Diabelli, Haydn, and others, see Unit 17.

Largo

6.

Con spirito

7.

Calmo

8.

Allegro

9.

Ben marcato

10.

Allegretto

11.

Ritmico

12.

Cantabile

13.

14.

15.

16.

17.

18.

Comodo 𝄋

Fine

D.S. al Fine

Melodic Dictation: QUIZ NO. 1

Andantino

1.

Allegro

2.

Pesante

3.

Moderato

4.

Allegretto

5.

Melodic Dictation: QUIZ NO. 2

Doloroso

1.

Allegro

2.

Cantabile

3.

Animato

4.

Class:

Professor:

Name: _____

5. Comodo

Class:

Professor:

Name: _____

Melodic Dictation: QUIZ NO. 3

Con moto

1.

Andantino

2.

Allegretto

3.

Andante

4.

Presto

5.

Harmonic Dictation: Modulation to Closely Related Keys

Phrase-Length Exercises

How is the first key established? Where does the key change? Is there a pivot chord? Is the new key confirmed cadentially? For examples of modulation to closely related keys in pieces by Bach, Diabelli, Haydn, and others, see Unit 17.

1.

B♭:I

2.

b:i

3.

G: I

4.

a: i

Class:

Name: _____

Professor:

5.

Eb: I

6.

f#: i

7.

D: I

8.

g: i

9.

Ab: I

10.

a: i

11.

G: I

12.

D: I

Class:

Name: _____

Professor:

13.

Ab:I

14.

b:iv⁷

15.

A: I

16.

c: i

17.

f: i

Name: _____

Harmonic Dictation: QUIZ NO. 1

1.

F: I

2.

f#: i

3.

C: I

4.

b: i

5.

B♭: I

Class:

Professor:

Name: _____

Harmonic Dictation: QUIZ NO. 2

1.

F: I

2.

b: i

3.

f: i

4.

A: I

5.

Eb: I

Class:

Professor:

Name: _____

Harmonic Dictation: QUIZ NO. 3

1.

c#: i

2.

Db: I

3.

d: i

4.

B♭: I

5.

G: I

Unit 16

Rhythmic Dictation: Quintuple Meter

Listen to each exercise while counting or tapping the beat. Is the organization of beats 3 + 2 or 2 + 3? Does it remain the same throughout or does it vary? Do you feel the pulse at the beat level or do you feel alternations of simple and compound divisions? Try adjusting the tempo. Does the speed of the music affect your perception?

Preliminary Exercises

1.

2.

3.

4.

5.

6.

Comprehensive Exercises

7.

8.

9.

10.

11.

12.

13.

14.

15.

16.

17.

18.

Class:

Name: _____

Professor:

Rhythmic Dictation: QUIZ NO. 1

1.

2.

3.

4.

5.

Rhythmic Dictation: QUIZ NO. 2

1.

2.

3.

4.

5.

Rhythmic Dictation: QUIZ NO. 3

1.

2.

3.

4.

5.

Melodic Dictation: The Neapolitan Sixth Chord, Augmented Sixth Chords, and Modulation to Distantly Related Keys

For examples of Neapolitan sixth chords, augmented sixth chords, and modulation to distantly related keys in pieces by Bach, Beethoven, and Schubert, see Unit 17.

Preliminary Exercises

1.

2.

3.

4.

5.

6.

7.

8.

Class: _____

Name: _____

Professor: _____

Melodies

These melodies emphasize the altered scale degrees associated with Neapolitan chords (including ♭2) and augmented sixth chords (including ♯4 and ♭6). Where are altered chords implied? What scale degrees seem most implicative? What structural lines do the altered scale degrees and the notes of resolution form? Are there arpeggiations? Does the melody modulate? Determine the new tonic. How is it established? Is there a logical pivot point or common tone, or does the music shift abruptly into the new key?

Andante

1.

Andantino

2.

Doloroso

3.

Marziale

4.

Moderato

5.

Andantino

6.

Allegro marcato

7.

Allegretto

8.

Class: _____   Name: _____

Professor: _____

Larghetto

9.

Giocoso

10.

Moderato

11.

Moderato

12.

Passionato

13.

Grazioso

14.

Fanfare

15.

Melodic Dictation: QUIZ NO. 1

Serioso

1.

Espressivo

2.

Calmo

3.

Con amore

4.

Class: _____

Professor: _____

Con passione

5.

Name: _____

Melodic Dictation: QUIZ NO. 2

Andantino

1.

Larghetto

2.

Allegro

3.

Andante

4.

Andantino

5.

Class:

Professor:

Name: _____

Melodic Dictation: QUIZ NO. 3

Amabile

1.

Grazioso

2.

Andantino

3.

4. Capriccioso

5. Comodo

Name: _____

Harmonic Dictation: The Neapolitan Sixth Chord, Augmented Sixth Chords, Enharmonic Modulation

Basic Progressions

1.

a: i

2.

B♭: I

3.

c: i⁶

4.

G: I

5.

c#: i

6.

B♭: I

7.

A♭: I

8.

C: I

9.

E: I

10.

d: i

Class: _____   Name: _____

Professor: _____

Phrase-Length Exercises

Drill on the Preliminary Exercises to establish the most common progressions using altered chords. Then listen to each phrase-length progression. Where do altered chords occur? Which voices have the altered scale degrees? Do the altered pitches resolve as expected? Do the phrases modulate? Concentrate on the way in which altered chords facilitate the modulation. For examples of Neapolitan sixth chords, augmented sixth chords, and modulation to distantly related keys in pieces by Bach, Beethoven, and Schubert, see Unit 17.

1. G: I

2. b: i

3. b: V♯

4. B♭: I

5.

C: I

6.

E♭: I

7.

F: I

8.

Bb: I

9.

g: i

10.

c#: i

11.

G: I

12.

Ab: I

13.

C: I

14.

Db: I

15.

G: I

Class: _____   Name: _____

Professor: _____

Harmonic Dictation: QUIZ NO. 1

1.

b: i

2.

A♭: I

3.

F: I

4.

C: I

Name: _____

5.

b: i

Harmonic Dictation: QUIZ NO. 2

1.

D: I

2.

b♭: i

3.

F: I

4.

f#: i

5.

c: i

Harmonic Dictation: QUIZ NO. 3

1.

f: i

2.

d: i

3.

e: i

4.

f♯: i

Class:

Professor:

Name: _____

5.

A: I

Unit 17

Examples from Music Literature

These exercises present actual musical examples for you to transcribe. All contain only the melodic and harmonic vocabulary studied so far and you should be able to transcribe each item completely. Listen to the example first. What is the texture? What kinds of cadences do you hear? Concentrate on individual lines and then listen harmonically. Isolate any altered chords. What are their functions? Does the music modulate? How are the keys established?

1. Johann Sebastian Bach. *Ach Gott, vom Himmel sieh' darein* (chorale)

2. Johann Sebastian Bach. *Befiehl du deine Wege* (chorale)

3. Johann Sebastian Bach. *Ach Gott, wie manches Herzeleid* (chorale)

4. Johann Sebastian Bach. *Hilf, Herr Jesu, lass gelingen* (chorale)

5. Johann Sebastian Bach. Bourrée, French Overture

Class:

Professor:

Name: _____

6. Jeremiah Clarke. Jigg

7. Antonio Diabelli. Rondino

Allegretto

8. Joseph Haydn. Sonata, Hob. XVI:27, mvt. III

Presto

9. Ludwig van Beethoven. Bagatelle, Op. 119, No. 1

10. Ludwig van Beethoven. Minuet in G Major, WoO 10, No. 2

Class: _____

Professor: _____

Name: _____

11. Mikail Ivanovich Glinka. Waltz, Op. 39, No. 15

12. Franz Schubert. Scherzo in B-flat

Name: _____

13. Joseph Haydn. Divertimento, Hob. II:18, mvt. III, Trio

14. Ludwig van Beethoven. Quartet, Op. 18, No. 1, mvt. III

Allegro molto

15. Ludwig van Beethoven. Quartet, Op. 18, No. 4, mvt. III

Allegretto

16. Ludwig van Beethoven. Quartet, Op. 18, No. 4, mvt. IV

17. Wolfgang Amadeus Mozart. Quartet, K. 421, mvt. III

Name: _____

18. Wolfgang Amadeus Mozart. Quartet, K. 170, mvt. I

Class:

Professor:

Name: _____

Name: _____

QUIZ NO. 1

1. Johann Sebastian Bach. *Befiehl du deine Wege* (chorale)

2. Domenico Scarlatti. Sonata, Longo 83

Name: _____

3. Joseph Haydn. Sonata, Hob. XVI:37, mvt. III

4. Ludwig van Beethoven. Sonata "Pathetique," Op. 13, mvt. III

QUIZ NO. 2

1. Johann Sebastian Bach. *Meine Seel' erhebt den Herren* (chorale)

2. Ludwig van Beethoven. Sonata, Op. 14, No. 1, mvt. II

Maggiore Allegretto

3. Johannes Brahms. Waltz, Op. 39, No. 15

Tempo giusto

4. Ludwig van Beethoven. Quartet, Op. 18, No. 2, mvt. III, Trio

TRIO   Allegro

Name: _____

QUIZ NO. 3

1. Johann Sebastian Bach. *Jesu, meine Freude* (chorale)

2. Robert Schumann. "Important Event," *Scenes from Childhood*, Op. 15, No. 6

3. Edvard Grieg. Rigaudon, Op. 40, No. 5, Trio

Allegro con brio *un poco meno mosso*

4. Ludwig van Beethoven. Quartet, Op. 18, No. 3, mvt. III

Allegro

Unit 18

Rhythmic Dictation: Irregular Meters

Listen for the groups of two and three notes. Do they form a regularly recurring pattern? The meter signature itself should suggest the possible groupings. Once you have established this basic grouping, focus on the values within the groups. Are there subdivisions? Syncopations?

1.

2.

3.

4.

5.

6.

7.

8.

9.

10.

11.

12.

13.

14.

Rhythmic Dictation: QUIZ NO. 1

1.

2.

3.

4.

5.

Rhythmic Dictation: QUIZ NO. 2

1.

2.

3.

4.

5.

Melodic Dictation: Diatonic Modes

Review the church modes, concentrating on the location of the half steps (semitones). Then listen to each melody. Is the mode "major" or "minor"? Is there a whole step or half step from degree 7 to 8? From degree 5 to 6? From degree 1 to 2? Does the melody both begin and end on the tonic? How is tonic established? Try singing the scale to establish the mode. Examples of modal usage in pieces by Bartók and Bloch can be found in Unit 26, Part 1.

Moderato bucolico

1.

Misterioso

2.

Tempo di valse

3.

Andante

4.

Con forza

5.

Cantabile

6.

Vigoroso

7.

Contempletivo

8.

Allegretto

9.

Grazioso

10.

Ruhig

11.

Scherzando

12.

Energico

13.

Andantino

14.

Class:

Professor:

Name: _____

Melodic Dictation: QUIZ NO. 1

Moderato

1.

Marcato

2.

Doloroso

3.

Ritmico

4.

Amabile

5.

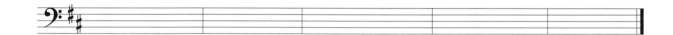

Melodic Dictation: QUIZ NO. 2

Gracieuse

1.

Vigoroso

2.

Andantino

3.

Allegretto

4.

Simply

5.

Class:

Professor:

Name: _____

Harmonic Dictation: Diatonic Modes

Review the qualities of the triads and seventh chords in each mode. As you listen to the exercises, first establish the mode. Is it "major" or "minor"? What is the quality of the dominant or dominant seventh? What particular progressions most clearly establish the mode? Identify the tonic and the specific mode. A Roman numeral functional analysis for each chord is no longer appropriate. Examples of modal usage in pieces by Bartók and Bloch can be found in Unit 26, Part 1.

1.

2.

3.

4.

5.

6.

7.

8.

9.

10.

11.

12.

13.

14.

Name: _____

Harmonic Dictation: QUIZ NO. 1

1.

2.

3.

4.

5.

Harmonic Dictation: QUIZ NO. 2

1.

2.

3.

4.

5.

Class:

Professor:

Name: _____

Unit 19

Rhythmic Dictation: Changing Meters

How does the pattern in each measure express the particular meter? Do recurring alternations of meters also show a recurring rhythmic pattern? How are cadences established?

1.

2.

3.

4.

5.

6.

7.

8.

9.

10.

11.

12.

13.

14.

Class: _____   Name: _____

Professor: _____

Rhythmic Dictation: QUIZ NO. 1

1.

2.

3.

4.

5.

Rhythmic Dictation: QUIZ NO. 2

1.

2.

3.

4.

5.

Part Music Dictation: Pandiatonicism

Focus on the individual lines. Is the motion conjunct or disjunct? Do you hear repetitions or *ostinati*, particularly in the lower voice? For an example of pandiatonicism in a piece by Stravinsky, see Unit 26, Part 1, no. 2.

Amabile

1.

Semplice

2.

Lent et grave

3.

Comodo

4.

Modéré

5.

Grazioso

6.

Andantino

7.

Follow the structural lines formed by the highest and/or lowest pitches of the patterns found in the upper voice.

Allegro

8.

Follow the structural lines formed by the highest and/or lowest pitches of the patterns found in the upper voice.

9.

Listen for intervallic planing in one or both voices. What interval is being used?

10.

Class: Name: _____

Professor:

Listen for intervallic planing in one or both voices. What interval is being used?

Giocoso

13.

Listen for two textural elements. Focus first on the bass line. Then listen to the three upper voices. What technique is being used?

Maestoso

14.

Listen for two textural elements. Focus first on the bass line. Then listen to the three upper voices. What technique is being used?

Stately

15.

Brilliante

16.

Part Music Dictation: QUIZ NO. 1

Piacevole

1.

Andante

2.

Class:

Name: _____

Professor:

Giocoso

3.

Sostenuto

4.

Fliessend

5.

Class:

Professor:

Name: _____

Part Music Dictation: QUIZ NO. 2

Tempo di Valse

1.

Allegretto

2.

Berceuse

3.

Moderato

4.

Moderato

5.

Name: _____

Unit 20

Rhythmic Dictation: Syncopation Including Irregular and Mixed Meters

Listen for syncopated accents occurring on weak beats or parts of beats. Does the syncopation occur at the beat level or at the division (or subdivision) level? Listen for uneven patterns of metrical accent that may suggest irregular or mixed meters. Recurring beat patterns such as 2+3 or 2+2+3 may occur. Some examples also employ triplets in simple meter or duplets in compound meter.

1.

2.

3.

4.

5.

Class:

Professor:

Name: _____

6.

7.

8.

9.

10.

456   Unit 20

11.

12.

13.

14.

Name: _____

Rhythmic Dictation: QUIZ NO. 1

1.

2.

3.

4.

5.

Rhythmic Dictation: QUIZ NO. 2

1.

2.

3.

4.

5.

Class: _____   Name: _____

Professor: _____

Melodic Dictation: Extended and Altered Tertian Harmony

These exercises are more challenging. Is there a tonal center? How is it established? Isolate the arpeggiations. What is the quality of the chord? What position is it in? Are tall chords implied? What is their quality? Then focus on scalar passages. Is a conventional scale suggested? A church mode? Or is the pattern
symmetrical or irregular? Examples of extended and altered tertian harmony in pieces by Debussy and
Carpenter can be found in Unit 26, Parts 1 and 2.

Moderato

5.

Grazioso

6.

Con moto

7.

Allegro ma non troppo

8.

Andante

9.

With a raggy feel

10.

Andante con moto

11.

Poco lento

12.

Risoluto

13.

Comodo

14.

Class:

Professor:

Name: _____

Melodic Dictation: QUIZ NO. 1

Piacevole

1.

Ritmico

2.

Amaroso

3.

Allegro vivace

4.

Serioso

5.

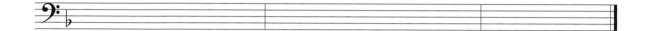

Class:

Professor:

Name: _____

Melodic Dictation: QUIZ NO. 2

Grazioso

1.

Moderato

2.

Moderato

3.

Scorrevole

4.

Tempo di valse

5.

Harmonic Dictation: Extended and Altered Tertian Harmony

These exercises present common, but often nonfunctional, progressions. Chordal extensions, such as the 9th, 11th, 13th, or added 6th are included. Focus on the qualities of each chord. Then work out the outer voices. Finally, fill in the inner voices. Chord symbols are now appropriate for analysis and should be placed above the treble staff as in sheet music or lead sheets. Examples of extended and altered tertian harmony in pieces by Debussy and Carpenter can be found in Unit 26, Parts 1 and 2.

5.

Several of the chords in the following exercise can be analyzed either as extended and altered dominants or as polychords. (See Unit 23.)

6.

7.

8.

9.

10.

11.

12.

13.

14.

Name: _____

Harmonic Dictation: QUIZ NO. 1

1.

2.

3.

4.

Dmaj7

5.

Harmonic Dictation: QUIZ NO. 2

Unit 21

Melodic Dictation: Exotic Scales

Is there a tonal center? How is it established? What scale is present in each exercise? What are the characteristic intervals of the scale? Are they prominent in the melody? For examples of exotic and artificial scales in pieces by Debussy, Stravinsky, Bartók, Carpenter, and Lasala, see Unit 26, Parts 1 and 2.

Inscrutably

1.

Moderato

2.

Vigoroso

3.

Alla inglese

4.

Moderato

5.

Lugubre

6.

Allegretto

7.

Lentement

8.

Misterioso

9.

Gracieux

10.

Melancholique

11.

Moderato

12.

Gracioso

13.

Con spirito

14.

Briskly

15.

Pensivo

16.

Semplice

17.

Class: _____   Name: _____

Professor: _____

Furious

18.

Very slow and sinuously

19.

Melodic Dictation: QUIZ NO. 1

Andantino

1.

Vif

2.

Moderato

3.

Im Volkston

4.

Andante tenebroso

5.

Class: _____

Name: _____

Professor: _____

Melodic Dictation: QUIZ NO. 2

Marcato

1.

Doucement

2.

Semplice

3.

Con espressione

4.

Con forza

5.

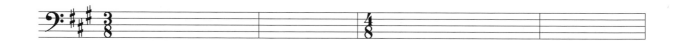

Part Music Dictation: Exotic Scales

Is there a tonal center? How is it established? What scale is present in each exercise? Do you hear repetitions of patterns? Ostinati? Imitation? What chord types are present? How are the chords connected? You do not need to provide a harmonic analysis. For examples of exotic and artificial scales in pieces by Debussy, Stravinsky, Bartók, Carpenter, and Lasala, see Unit 26, Parts 1 and 2.

Modéré

1.

Lento

2.

Grazioso

3.

Assez lentment

4.

Comodo

5.

Adagio

8.

Chorale

9.

Allegro moderato

10.

Part Music Dictation: QUIZ NO. 1

Andantino

1.

Lugubre

2.

3.

Part Music Dictation: QUIZ NO. 2

Scherzando

1.

Moderato

2.

Tempo di Valse

3.

Unit 22

Melodic Dictation: Quartal Harmony

These exercises focus on patterns using fourths and fifths. Is there a tonal center? How is it established? Isolate the scalar fragments. What is the pattern of whole and half step? Are conventional scales suggested? Exotic or symmetrical? For examples of quartal harmony in pieces by Stravinsky and Debussy, see Unit 26, Part 1.

Nicht zu schnell

1.

Feierlich

2.

Sehr langsam

3.

Fanfaro

4.

Name: _____

Lento

5.

Grazioso

6.

Lebhaft

7.

Gondellied

8.

Con fuoco

9.

Con forza

10.

Con tristezza

11.

Intenso

12.

Allegretto

13.

Maestoso

14.

Langsam aber nicht schleppend

15.

Melodic Dictation: QUIZ NO. 1

1. Zart

2. Lebhaft

3. Gesangvoll

4. Vivace

Melancholique

5.

Melodic Dictation: QUIZ NO. 2

Con moto

1.

Commodo

2.

Pesante

3.

Scherzando

4.

Giocoso

5.

Class: _____   Name: _____

Professor: _____

Part Music Dictation: Quartal Harmony

Is there a tonal center? How is it established? Concentrate on the individual voices. Do major or minor triads occur? Where? How are chords connected? You do not need to provide a harmonic analysis. For examples of quartal harmony in pieces by Stravinsky and Debussy, see Unit 26, Part 1.

Solenne

1.

Semplice

2.

Lullaby

3.

Etwas langsam

4.

Allegretto

5.

Chorale

6.

Moderato

7.

Stately

8.

What technique is employed in the upper voices?

Molto sostenuto

9.

Breit

10.

Part Music Dictation: QUIZ NO. 1

Lento

Maestoso

Comodo

Larghetto

Maestoso

5.

Class:

Professor:

Name: _____

Part Music Dictation: QUIZ NO. 2

1.

Moderato

2.
Con moto

3.
Andantino

4.
Amabile

Unit 23

Part Music Dictation: Polyharmony and Polytonality

For examples of polyharmony and polytonality by Bartók, see Unit 26, Part 2.

What scale is suggested in each part? What device is employed in the lower voice?

1.

What technique is being employed here?

2.

Is there a tonal center? How is it established? What is the basic chord type?

3.

Commodo

4.

Sustained

5.

Semplice

6.

Allegro

7.

Maestoso

8.

Rakishly

9.

10.

11.

Vigoroso

12.

Nostalgico

13.

14.

Class:

Name: _____

Professor:

Part Music Dictation: QUIZ NO. 1

Piacevole

1.

Grave

2.

Allegro ma no troppo

3.

Vivace

4.

Allegretto

5.

Part Music Dictation: QUIZ NO. 2

Moderato

1.

Tempo di Tango

2.

Maestoso

3.

Doloroso

4.

Class:

Name: _____

Professor:

Majestically

5.

Unit 24

Melodic Dictation: Interval Music

Preliminary Exercises

These exercises will seriously test your ability to hear intervals! Focus on cells of three to four notes. Is
there a pattern? Does this pattern recur? What is the interval connecting the recurrences (interval of trans-
position)? Are there permutations of intervals within the cell? Examples of interval music by Stravinsky,
Bartók, Sessions, and Schoenberg can be found in Unit 26, Part 3.

1.

2.

3.

4.

5.

6.

7.

8.

In these next two examples, listen for the wedge shape.

9.

10.

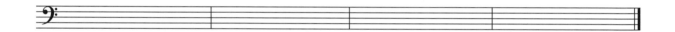

Melodies

Are there obvious sets or cells? Do you hear recurrences or transpositions? Are there permutations of intervals within the cells? Examples of interval music by Stravinsky, Bartók, Sessions, and Schoenberg can be found in Unit 26, Part 3.

Andantino

1.

Allegretto

2.

Gesangvoll

3.

Scherzando

4.

Alla Marcia

5.

Massig

6.

Assez vite

7.

Feierlich

8.

Andantino

9.

Agitato

10.

Deliberamente

11.

Molto con brio

12.

Scherzando

13.

Sinuously

14.

Class:

Professor:

Name: _____

Melodic Dictation: QUIZ NO. 1

Lento

1.

Lullaby

2.

Heftig

3.

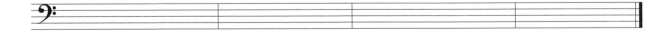

Allegro ma non troppo

4.

Lugubre

5.

Class:

Name: _____

Professor:

Melodic Dictation: QUIZ NO. 2

Scherzando

1.

Larghetto

2.

Strepitoso

3.

Agitato

4.

Moderato

5.

Unit 25

Melodic Dictation: Serial Music

Are there cells or sets within the rows? Are there any "anchors" such as repetition or recurrence of pitches or intervals in the same register to help you "solve" these exercises? Examples of serial music by Schoenberg, Dallapicolla, and Webern can be found in Unit 26, Part 3.

Scherzando

1.

Schleppend

2.

Avec mouvement

3.

Giocoso

4.

Con forza

5.

Sinuously

6.

Moderato

7.

Freely

8.

Animato

9.

Molto lento e calmo

10.

Heftig

11.

Deliberamente

12.

Melodic Dictation: QUIZ NO. 1

Fliessend

1.

Allegro

2.

Con espressione

3.

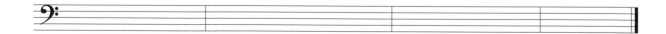

Class:

Professor:

Name: _____

Melodic Dictation: QUIZ NO. 2

Con moto

1.

Andantino

2.

Mässig

3.

Melodic Dictation: Serial Music   535

Unit 26

Examples from Music Literature

Part 1: Modality, pandiatoniscism, free tertian

These exercises present actual music for you to transcribe. All contain only the melodic and harmonic vocabulary studied in Units 18–25 and you should be able to transcribe each item completely. Listen to the example first. What is the texture? Concentrate on individual lines. What is the scale or mode? Then listen harmonically. What kinds of chord structures are employed? Are chords connected traditionally or is some contemporary device such as planing used? Is the music tonal? How is the sense of tonal center established? Are there obvious candences?

1. Béla Bartók, Evening in the Country

2. Igor Stravinsky, Vivo

3. Ernst Bloch, Waves, mm. 71–78

4. Claude Debussy, Prelude VIII, mm. 24–28

Très calme et doucement expressif

5. Claude Debussy, Sarabande, mm. 23–29

Avec une élégance grave et lente

Name: _____

6. Igor Stravinsky, *L'Histoire du Soldat*, "Marche Royale"

QUIZ NO. 1

1. Carlos Chávez, Prelude No. 2

2. Claude Debussy, Rêverie, mm. 51–58

3. Igor Stravinsky, *L'Histoire du Soldat*, Petit Choral

4. Bronislau Kaper, Green Dolphin Street

Part 2: Scalar and chordal techniques, polytonality

1. Bela Bartók, Sketches, II (See-saw . . .)

2. Béla Bartók, Sketches, V (Roumanian Folk Song)

3. John Alden Carpenter, Danza, mm. 193–198

4. Ángel Lasala, Trío No. 1, I, mm. 77–82

QUIZ NO. 2

1. Béla Bartók, Bear Dance

2. Béla Bartók, Forty-four Violin Duets, No. 33, Harvest Song

Part 3: Interval music, free atonality, and serialism

These exercises will require you to focus on hearing intervals. You may wish to review the interval exercises in Unit 1 and the web-based interval exercises. Listen for recurring motives of three or four notes. Is there evidence of twelve-tone serialism?

1. Igor Stravinsky, Symphony of Psalms, II

2. Béla Bartók, Music for Strings, Percussion, and Celesta, I

3. Arnold Schoenberg, Three Songs

4. Luigi Dallapiccola, Goethe Lieder, Mvt. 2

5. Roger Sessions, Sonata for Violin

Tempo moderato, con ampiezza e liberamente (♩=c.66)

6. Arnold Schoenberg, Drei Klavierstück, Op. 11, No. 1

Mäßige ♩

rit.

7. Anton Webern, Symphony, Op. 21, II, Variationen, Thema

* The harmonics (∘) in the Harp sound an octave higher than written.

QUIZ NO. 3

1. Edgard Varèse, Octandre, I

Assez lent (♩=63–66)

mp

2. Ernst Krenek, Suite for Violoncello Solo

Andante affettuoso (♩=72)

p

accel.   *a tempo*   **Più lento** (♩=60)

3. Luigi Dallapiccola, Quaderno Musicale di Annalibera, I

Quasi lento (♪=84) *mf sost.*

mp staccatiss.